MUSIC 785.11/ WAL

LONDON BOROUGH OF SOUTHWARK
ADULT LIBRARIES

DULWICH LIBRARY
368 Lordship Lane
London SE22 8NB
Tel: 020 7525 2000

PLEASE RETURN OR RENEW THIS ITEM BY THE LAST DATE STAMPED

This book is due for return on or before the latest date marked below. A charge will be made if it is retained for a longer period. Books may be renewed if not required by another reader. Not more than two such renewals may be made by post or telephone and the latest date and the book number must be quoted.

Opening hours are displayed in the library.

25. JUN. 1992		
25 MAR 1995	-2 JUN 2006	
2 6 SEP 1996	24 JUN 2008	
-4 NOV 1996		
1 1 SEP 1998		
1 6 AUG 1999		
	-5 APR 2002	
2 2 NOV 2005		

FINES

WILLIAM WALTON

SYMPHONY

FULL SCORE

OXFORD UNIVERSITY PRESS

ORCHESTRATION

2 Flutes	3 Trumpets
(2nd doubling Piccolo)	3 Trombones
2 Oboes	Tuba
2 Clarinets	Timpani (2 players)
2 Bassoons	Percussion (2 players)
4 Horns	Strings

Approximate duration, 43 minutes.

The orchestral material, including large scores for conducting, is on hire from the Publishers.

This Symphony was first performed in its entirety on 6 November 1935 at a B.B.C. Symphony Concert in Queen's Hall, conducted by Sir Hamilton Harty.

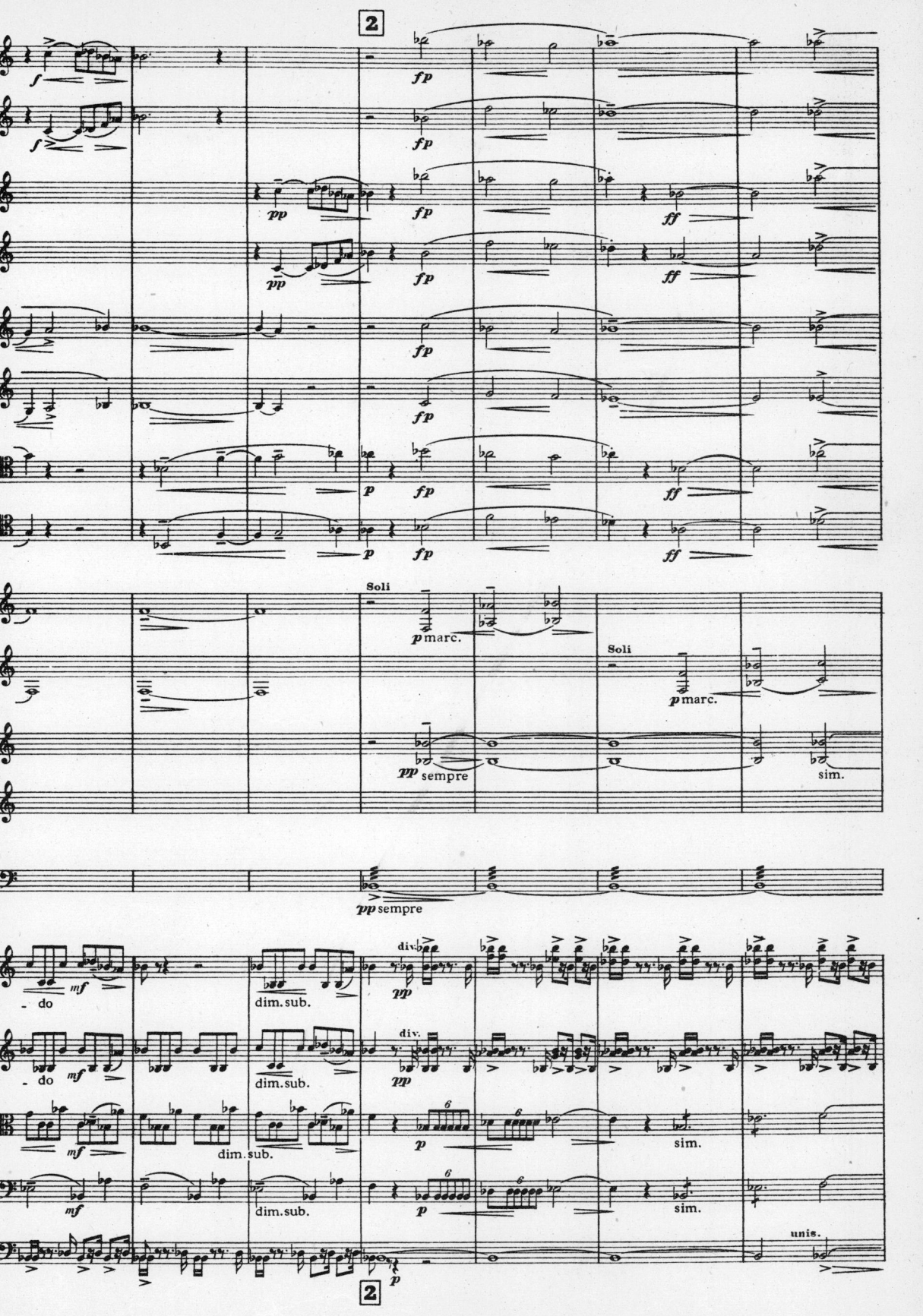

16

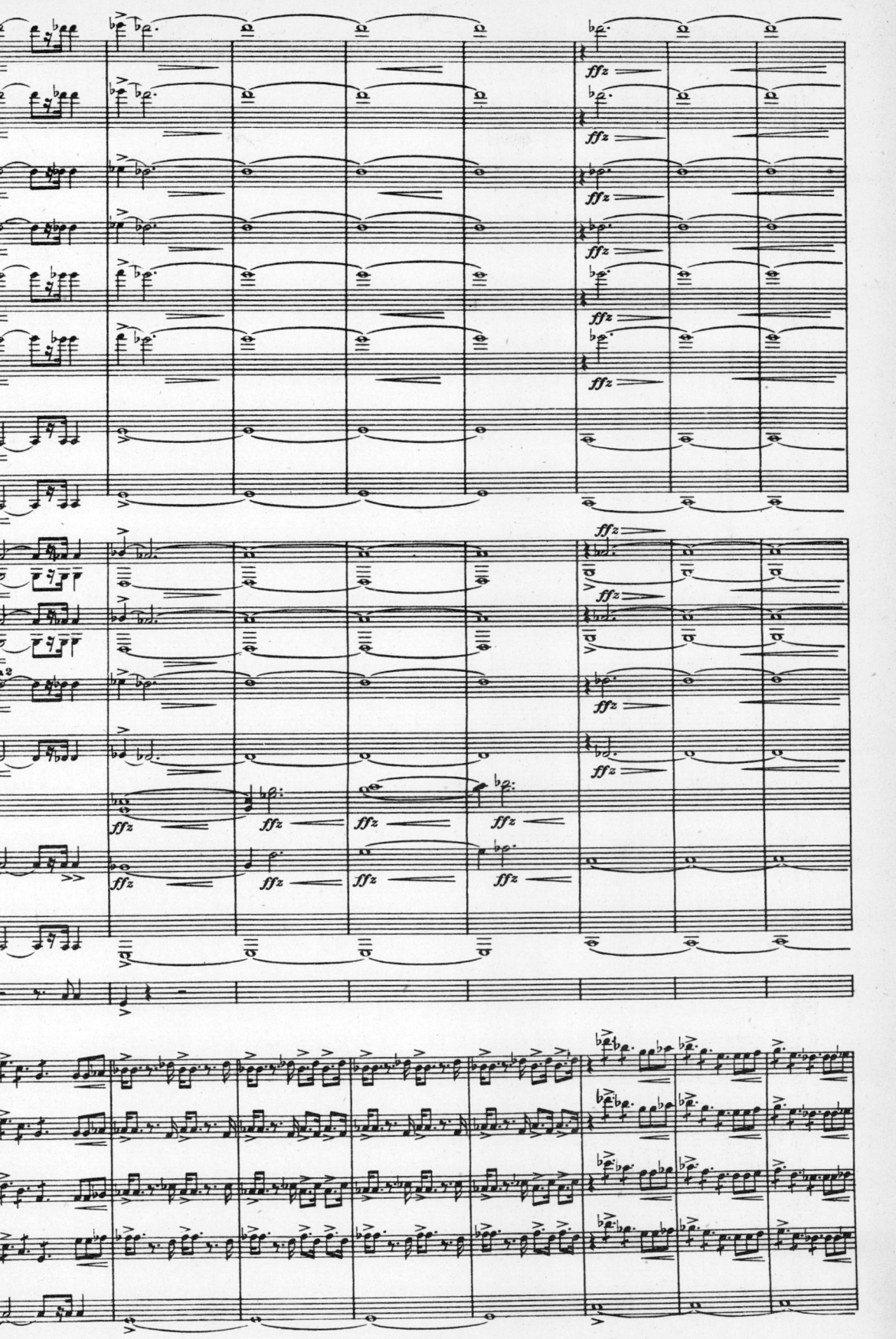

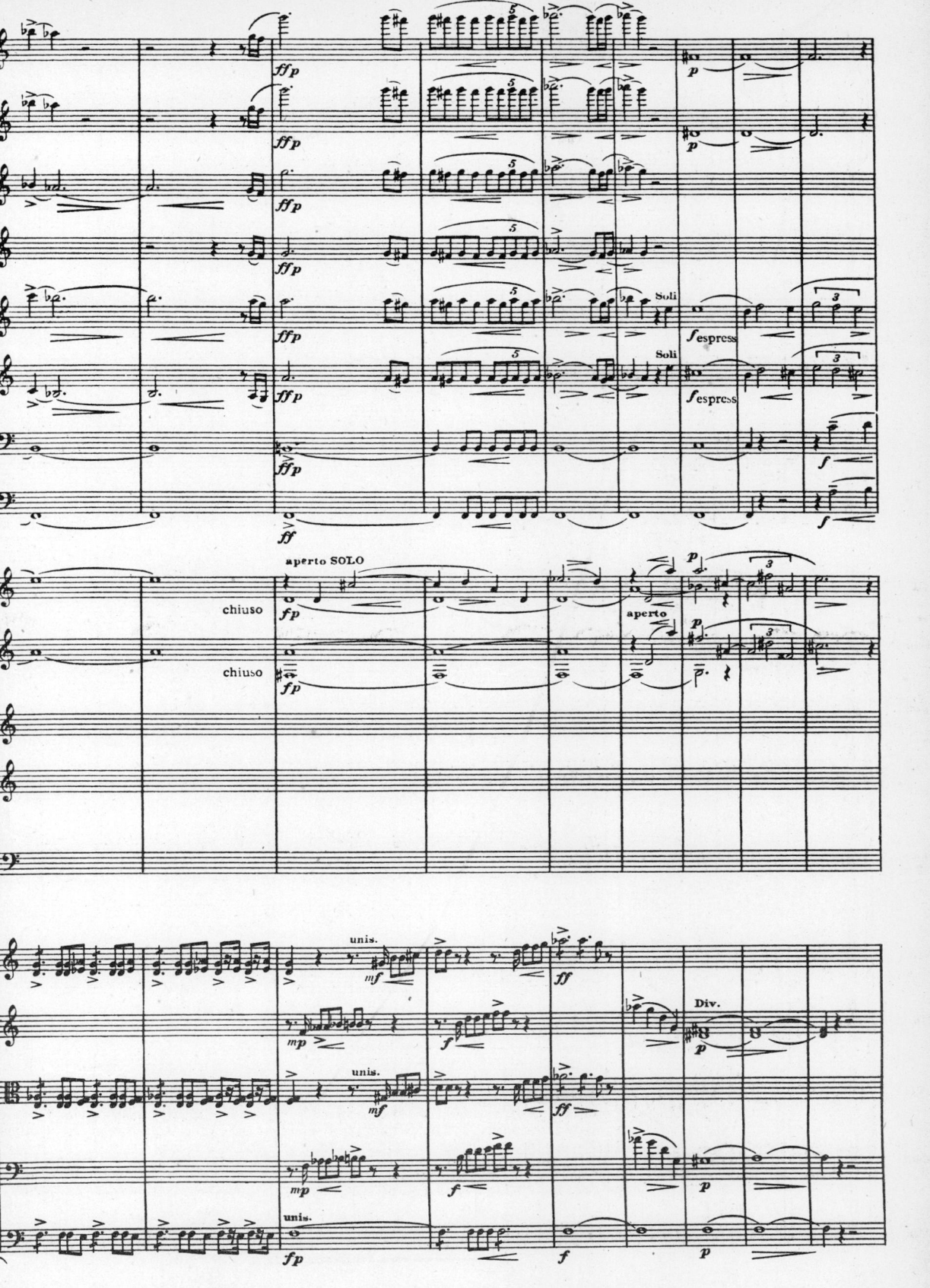

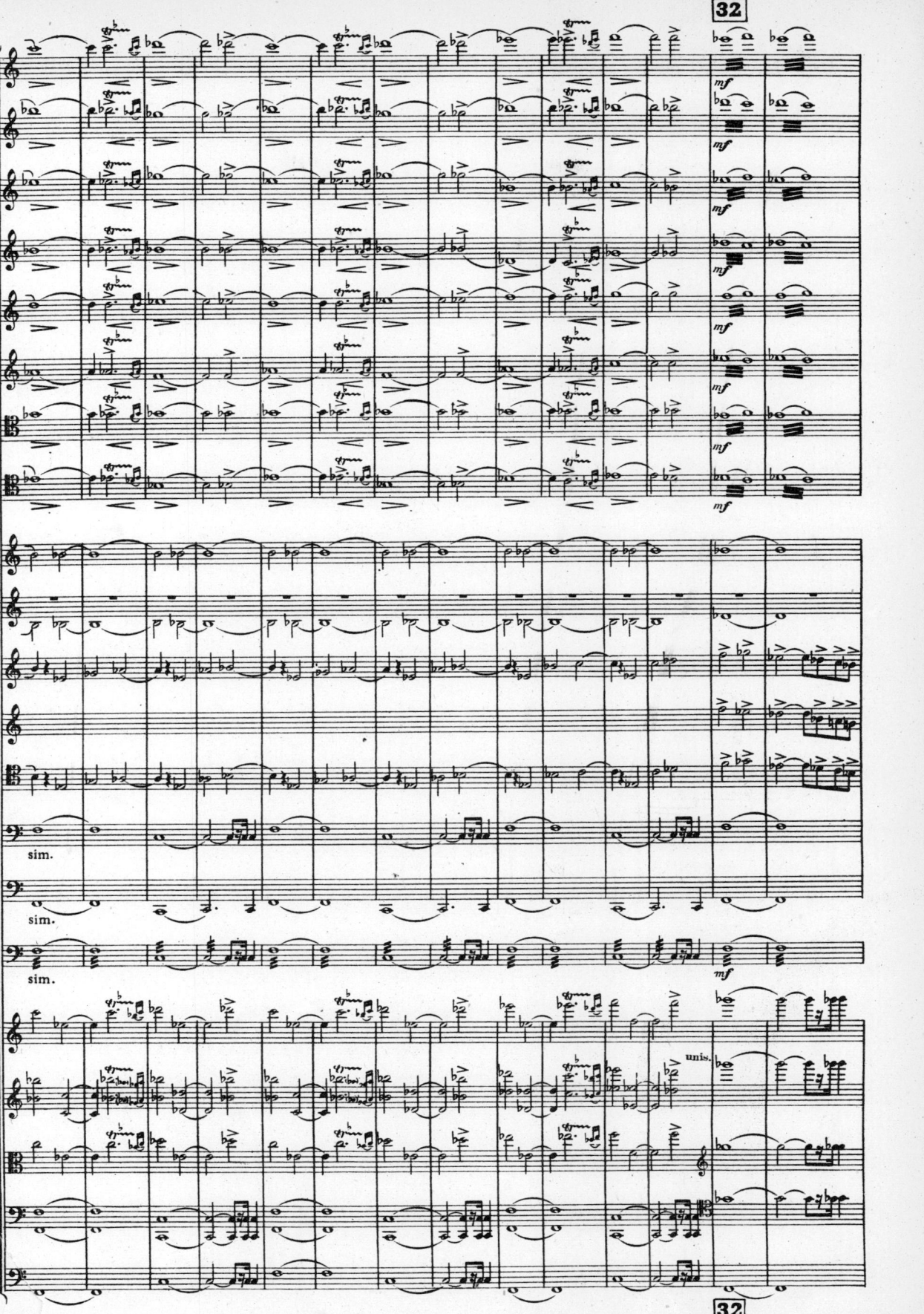

II

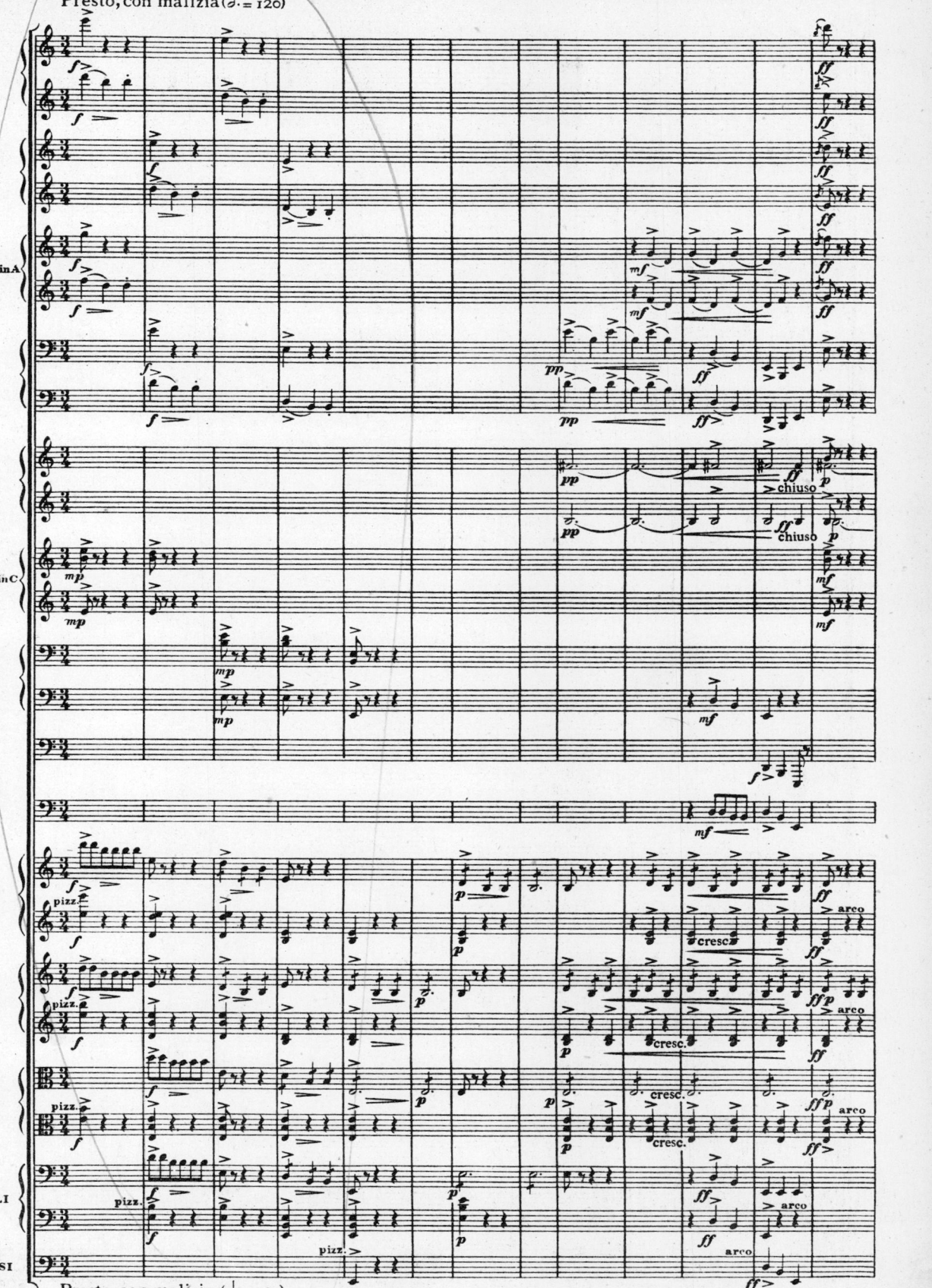

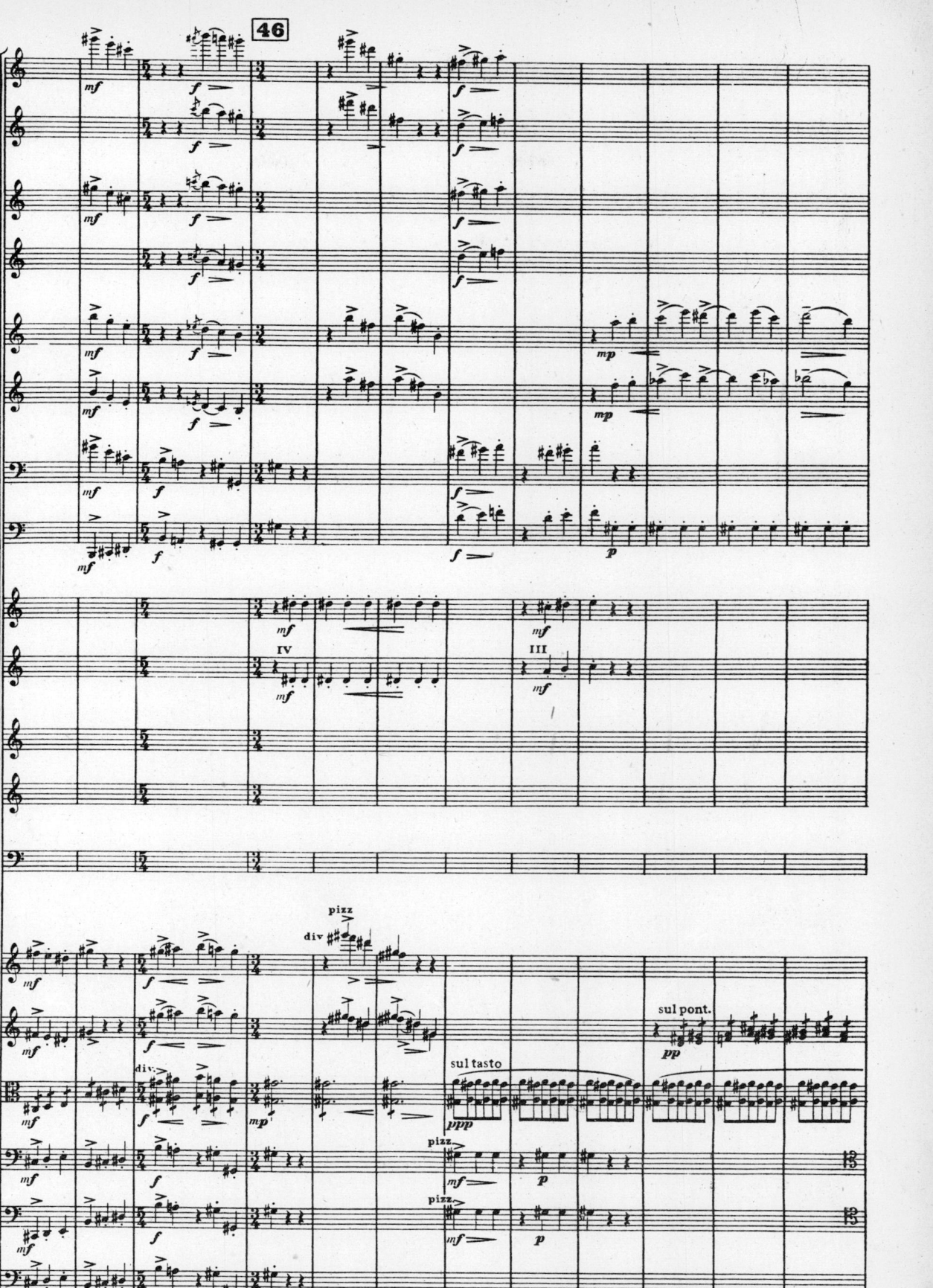

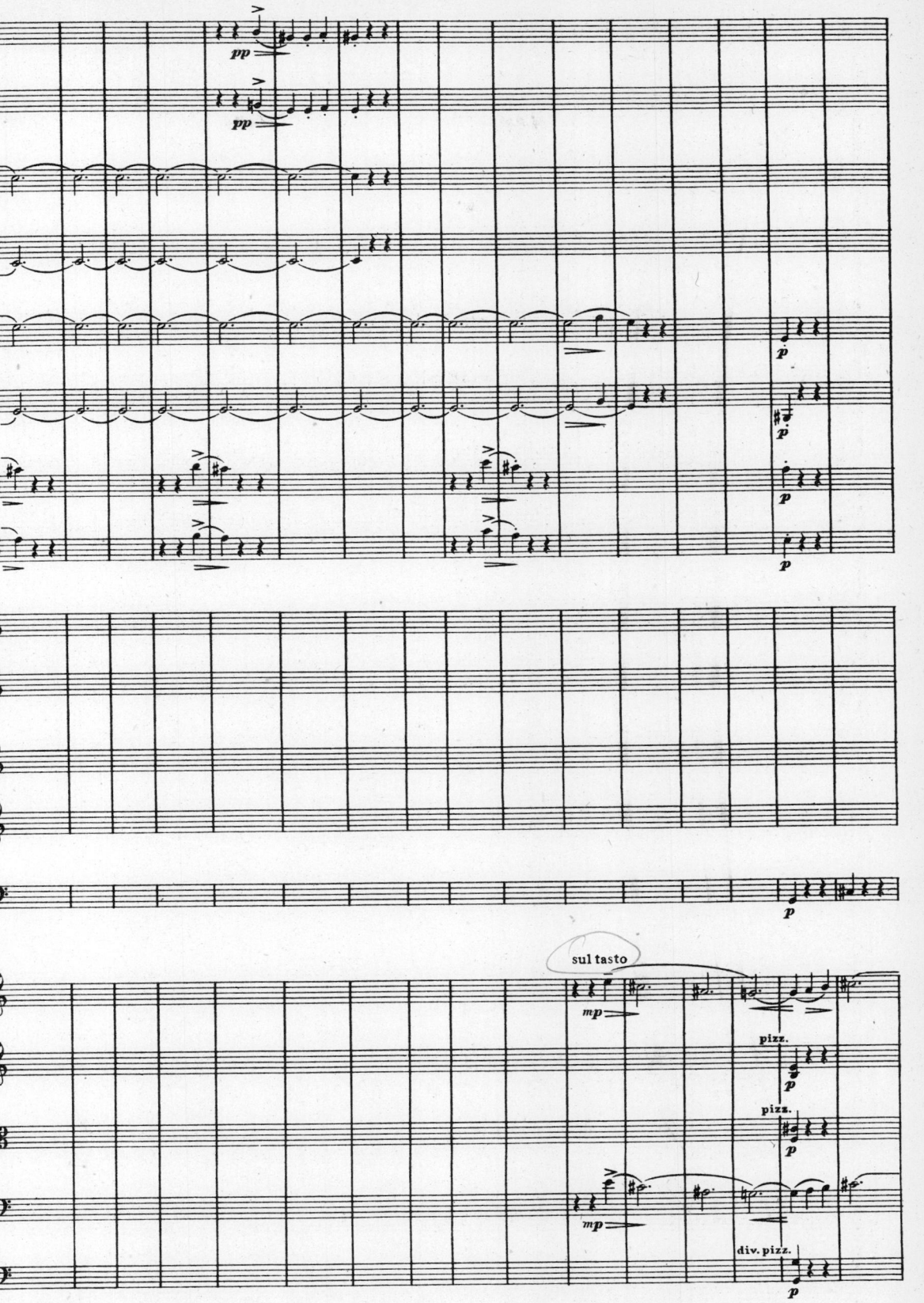

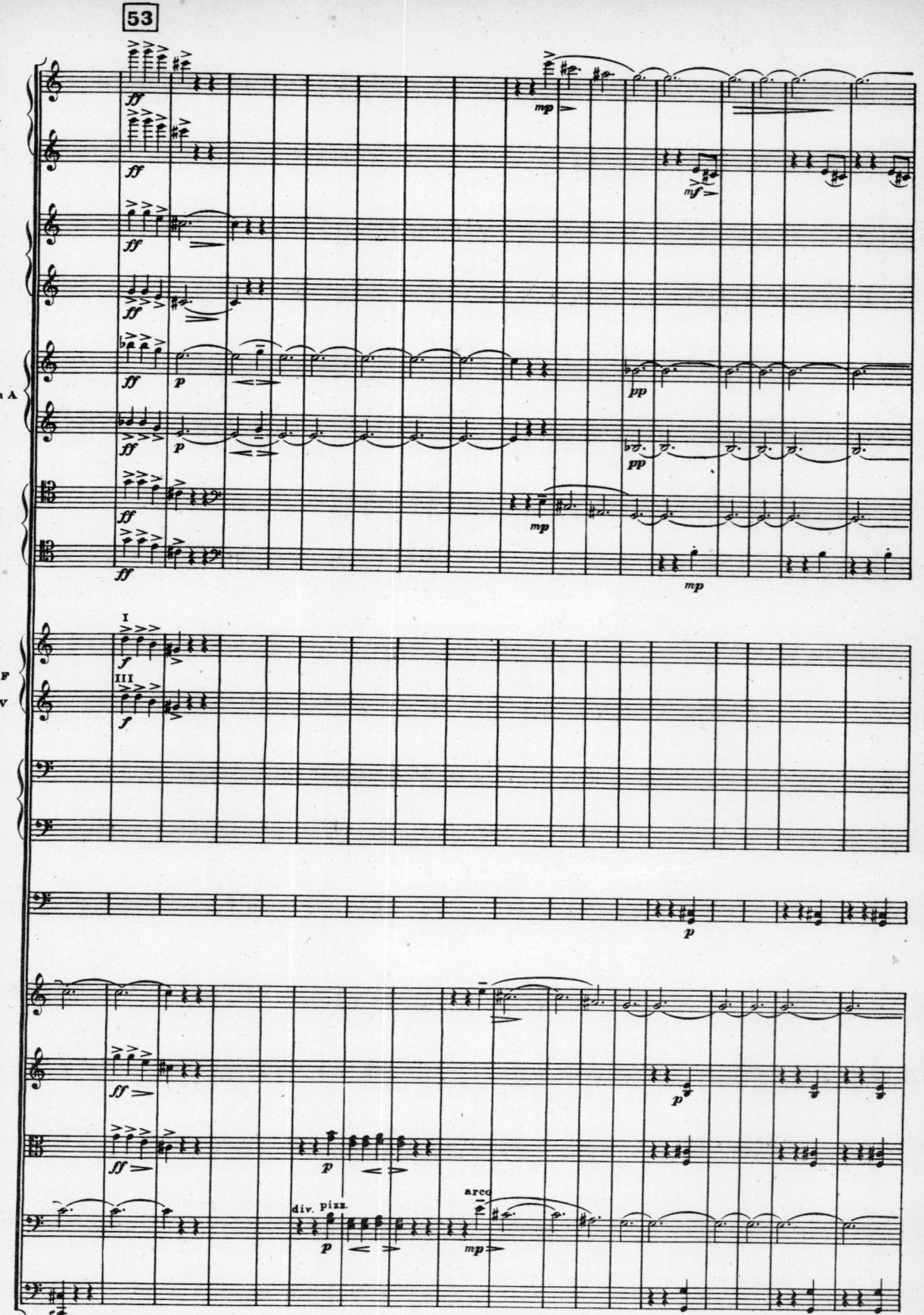

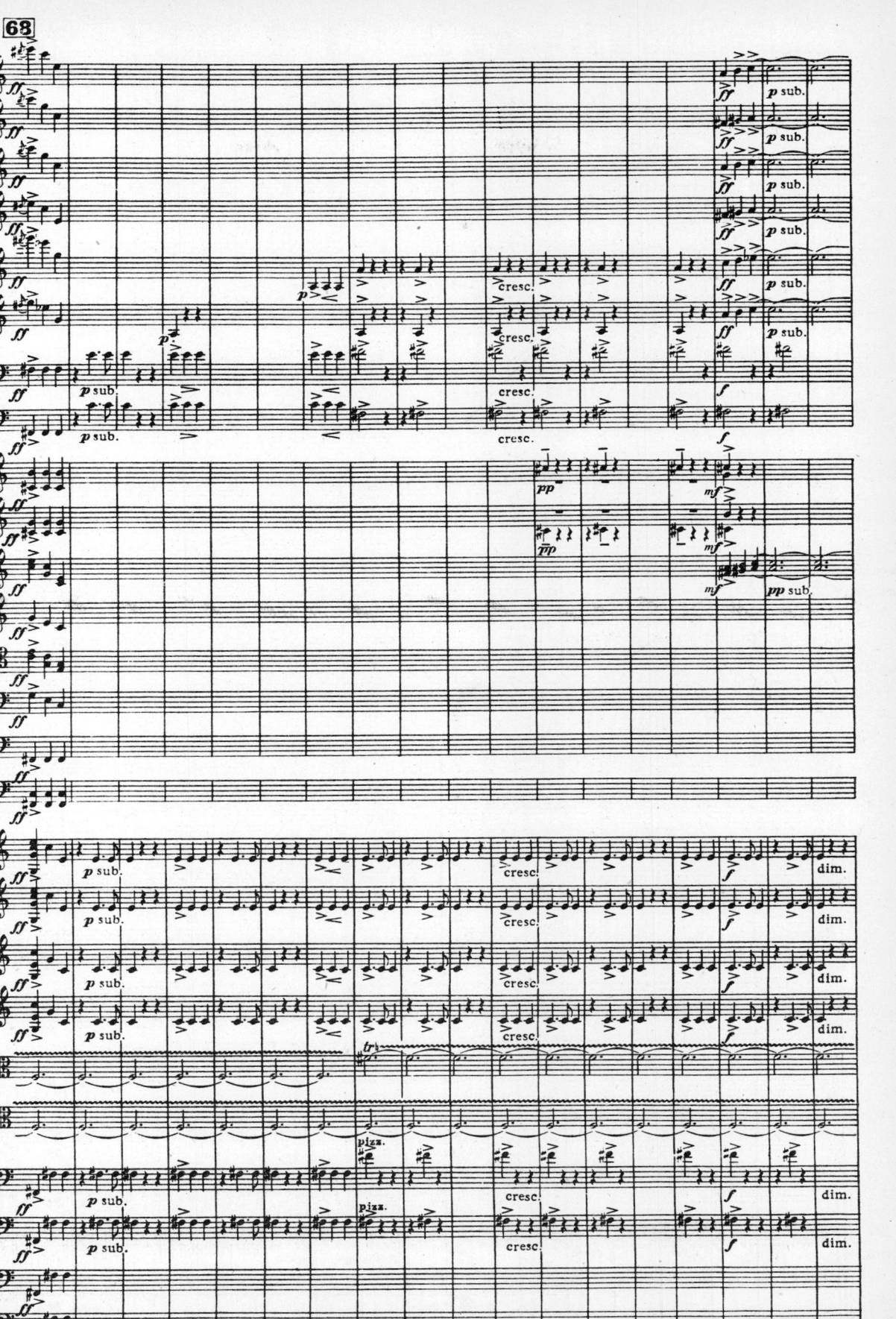

III

III

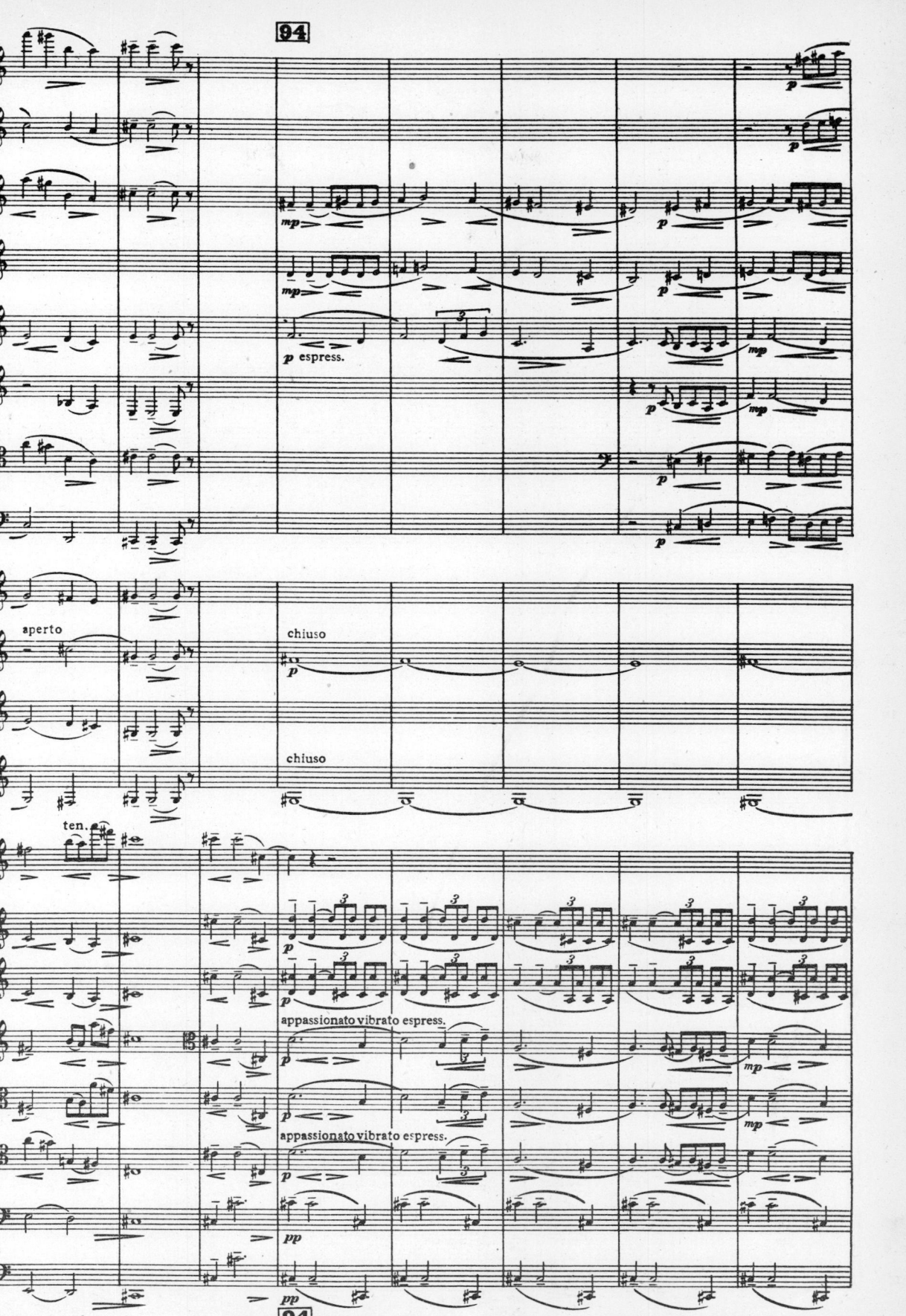

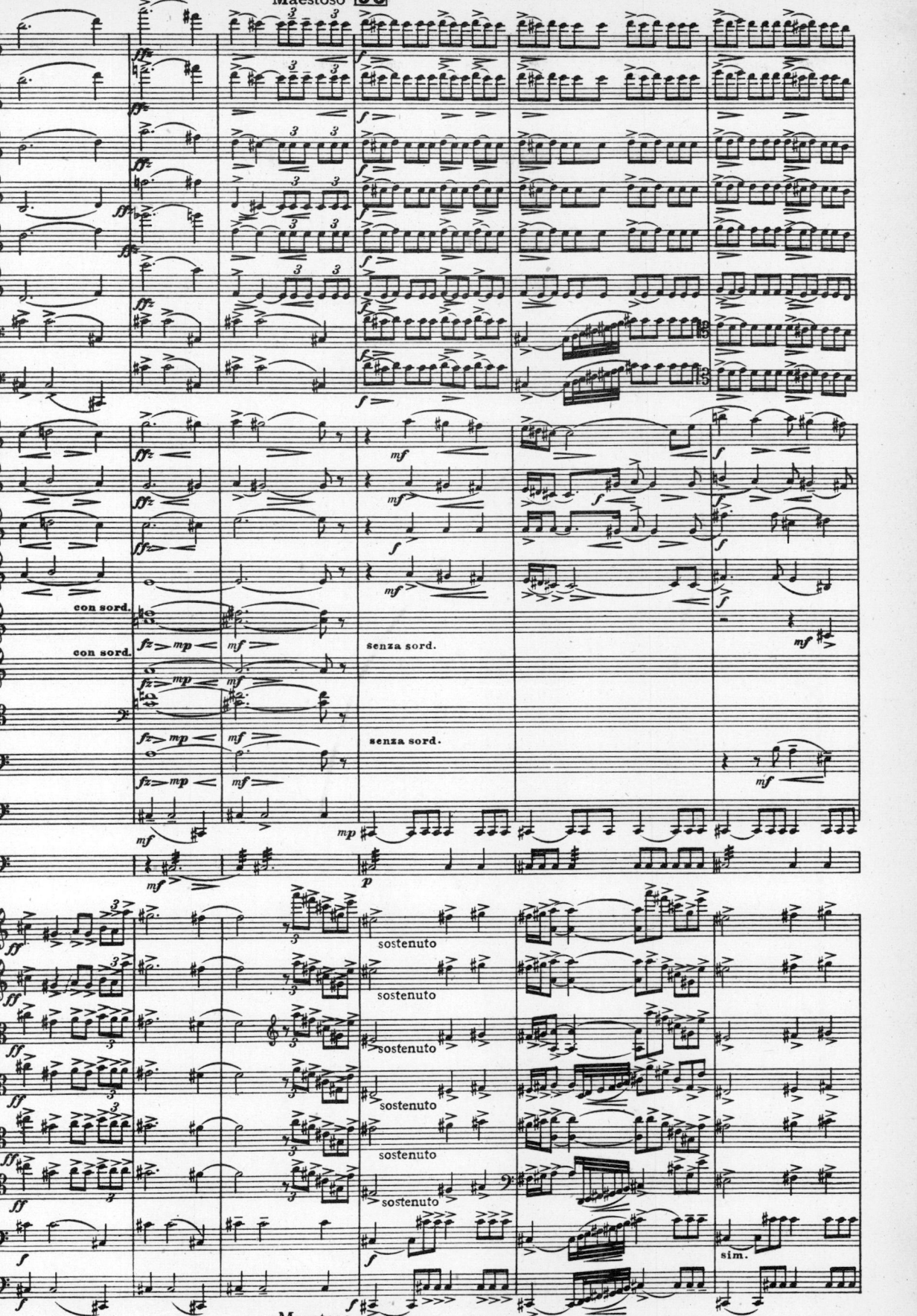

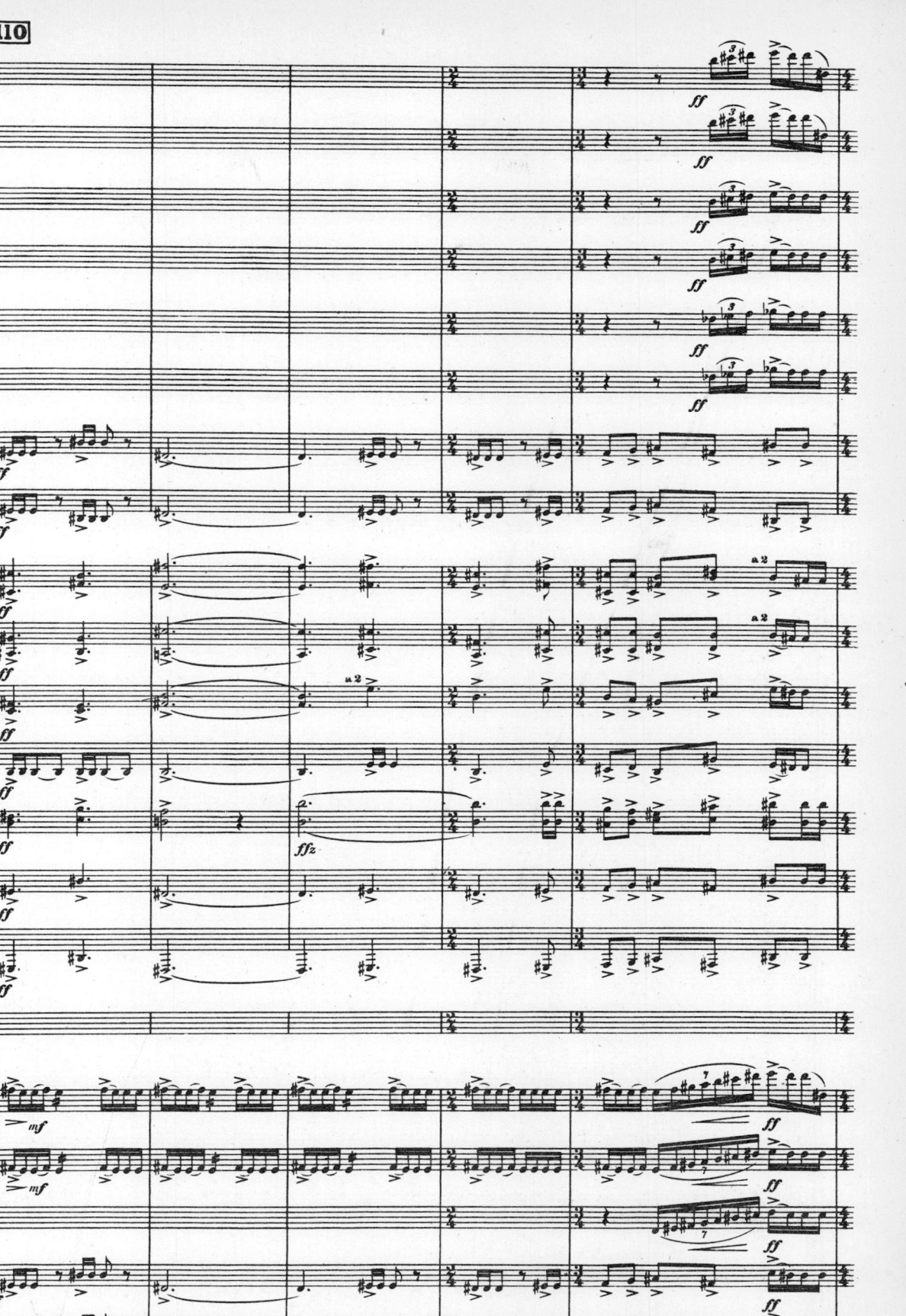

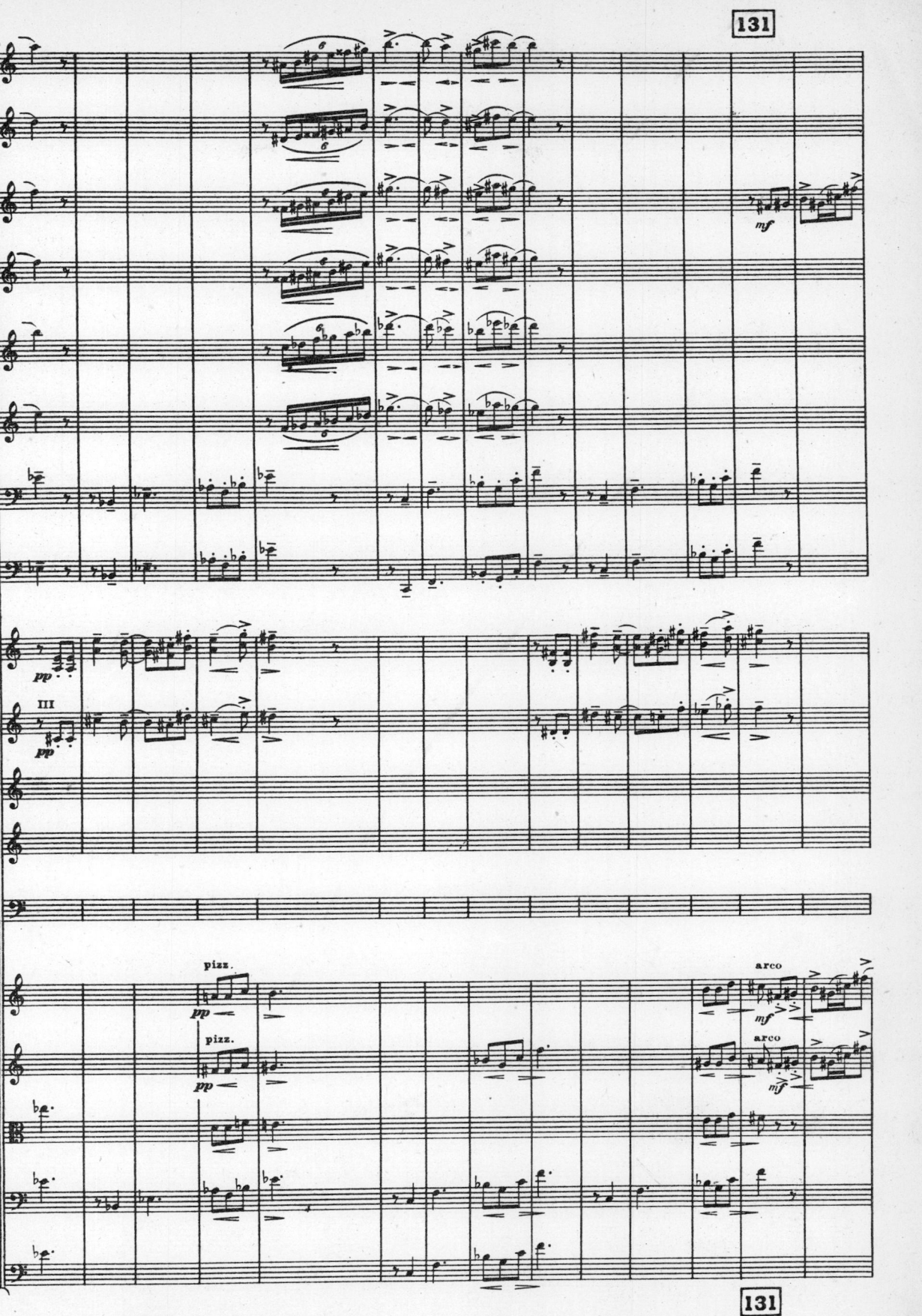

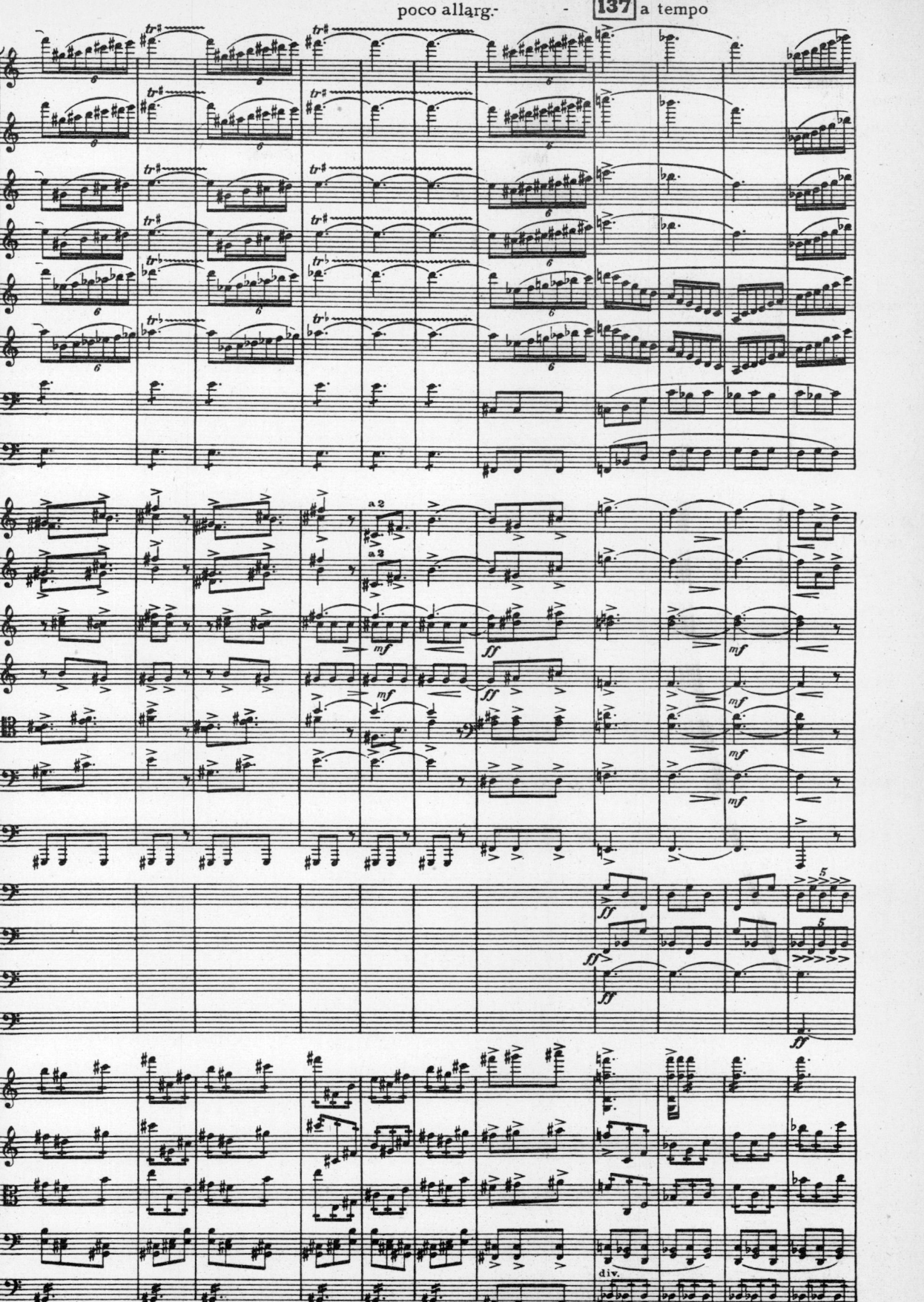